Matthew's book

with love from

Grandy and Opapa O.

FIFTY FAVORITE NURSERY RHYMES

Compiled and edited by Leslie Carola

Illustrations by Maura Conron

LONGMEADOW PRESS

HEY, DIDDLE, DIDDLE

Hey, diddle, diddle,
The cat and the fiddle;
The cow jumped over the moon.
The little dog laughed
To see such craft;
And the dish ran away with the spoon.

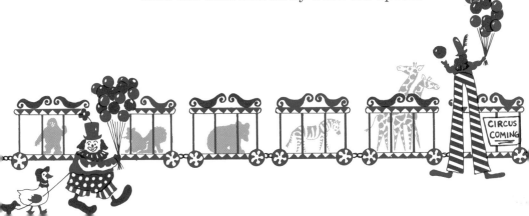

CIRCUS COMING

OLD KING COLE

Old King Cole was a merry old soul,
And a merry old soul was he;
He called for his pipe,
And he called for his bowl,
And he called for his fiddlers three.
Oh, there's none so rare, as can compare
With King Cole and his fiddlers three!

CIRCUS
GOING

SEE A PENNY

See a penny, pick it up,
All the day you'll have good luck;
See a penny, let it lay,
Bad luck you'll have all day.

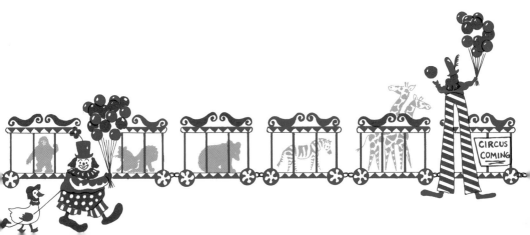

JACK SPRAT

Jack Sprat could eat no fat,
His wife could eat no lean;
And so, between the two of them
They licked the platter clean.

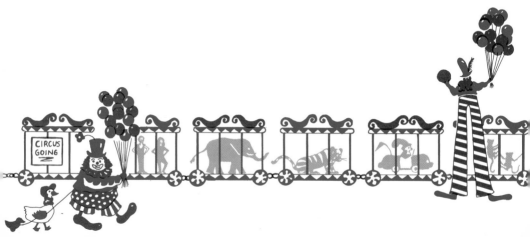

PUSSY CAT

Pussy cat, pussy cat, where have you been?
I've been up to London to visit the queen.
Pussy cat, pussy cat, what did you there?
I frightened a little mouse under the chair.

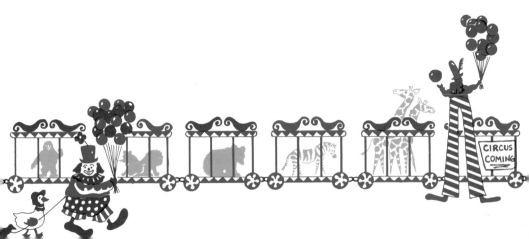

A DILLER, A DOLLAR

A diller, a dollar,
A ten o'clock scholar,
What makes you come so soon?
You used to come at ten o'clock,
But now you come at noon.

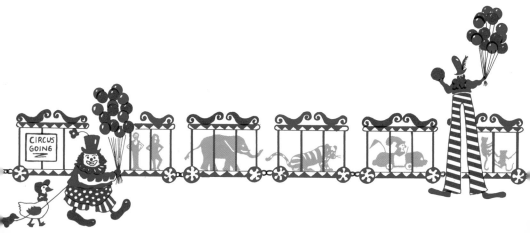

HECTOR PROTECTOR

Hector Protector was dressed all in green;
Hector Protector was sent to the Queen.
The Queen did not like him,
No more did the King:
So Hector Protector was sent back again.

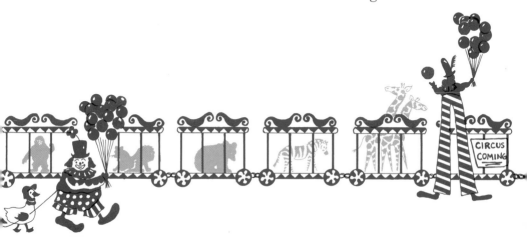

SEE, SAW, MARGERY DAW

See, Saw, Margery Daw,
Sold her bed and lay on the straw:
Wasn't she a silly bird,
To sell her bed and lie in the dirt!

PAT-A-CAKE, PAT-A-CAKE

Pat-a-cake, pat-a-cake, baker's man!
Make me a cake as fast as you can:
Pat it, and prick it, and mark it with a "B,"
Put it in the oven for Baby and me.

LADYBUG, LADYBUG

Ladybug, ladybug,
Fly away home,
Your house is on fire
And your children are gone.

LITTLE BOY BLUE

Little Boy Blue, go blow your horn,
The sheep's in the meadow,
The cow's in the corn.
Where's the little boy that tends the sheep?
He's under the haystack fast asleep.

HUMPTY DUMPTY

Humpty Dumpty sat on a wall,
Humpty Dumpty had a great fall,
All the King's horses
And all the King's men
Couldn't put Humpty together again.

THREE BLIND MICE

Three blind mice, see how they run!
They all run after the farmer's wife,
Who cut off their tails with a carving-knife.
Did you ever see such a sight in your life,
As three blind mice?

DIDDLE, DIDDLE DUMPLING

Diddle, diddle dumpling, my son John,
Went to bed with his britches on,
One shoe off, and one shoe on:
Diddle, diddle dumpling, my son John.

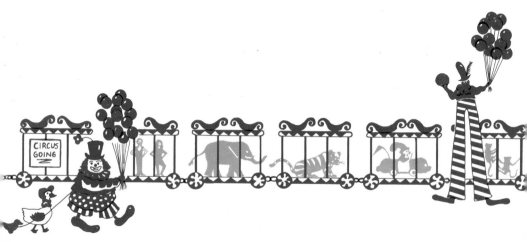

RAIN, RAIN GO AWAY

Rain, rain, go away;
Come again another day;
Little Suzie wants to play.

LITTLE JACK HORNER

Little Jack Horner sat in a corner
Eating his Christmas pie.
He put in his thumb and pulled out a plum
And said "What a good boy am I."

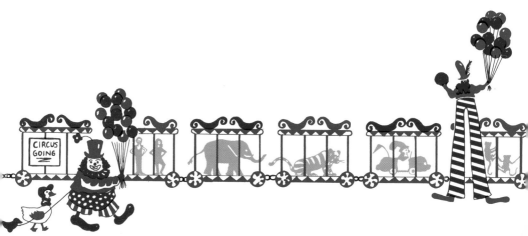

EARLY TO BED

Early to bed, and early to rise,
Makes a man healthy, wealthy, and wise.

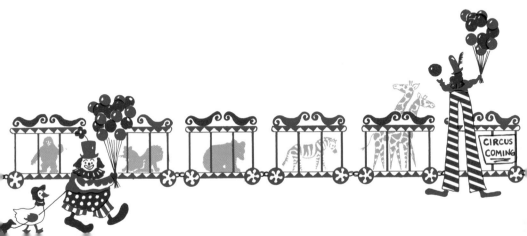

POLLY, PUT THE KETTLE ON

Polly, put the kettle on, kettle on, kettle on,
Polly, put the kettle on, we'll all have tea.

Sukey, take it off again, off again, off again,
Sukey, take it off again, they've all gone away.

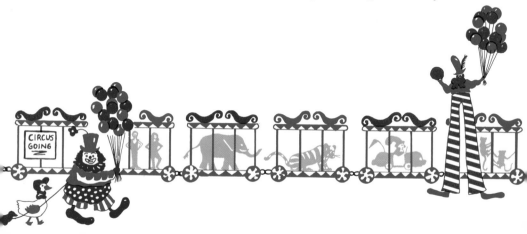

HOT CROSS BUNS

Hot cross buns!
Hot cross buns!
One a penny, two a penny
Hot cross buns!

Hot cross buns!
Hot cross buns!
If you have no daughters,
Give them to your sons.

DOCTOR FOSTER

Doctor Foster went to Gloucester,
In a shower of rain;
He stepped in a puddle, up to his middle,
And never went there again.

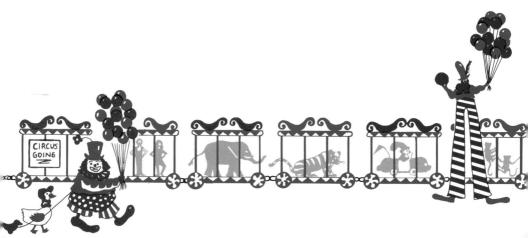

YANKEE DOODLE

Yankee Doodle went to town,
Riding on a pony;
He stuck a feather in his hat,
And called it Macaroni.

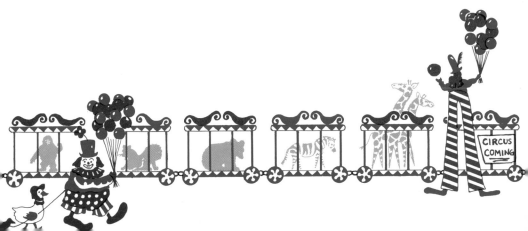

TWINKLE, TWINKLE, LITTLE STAR

Twinkle, twinkle, little star
How I wonder what you are,
Up above the world so high,
Like a diamond in the sky.

When the blazing sun is gone,
When he nothing shines upon,
Then you show your little light,
Twinkle, twinkle, all the night.

In the dark blue sky you keep,
Often through my curtains peep,
For you never shut your eye,
Till the sun is in the sky.

As your bright and tiny spark
Lights the traveler in the dark,
Though I know not what you are,
Twinkle, twinkle, little star.

CIRCUS
COMING

THREE MEN IN A TUB

Rub-a-dub-dub, three men in a tub,
And who do you think they be?
The butcher, the baker, the candlestick maker,
And all had come from the fair.

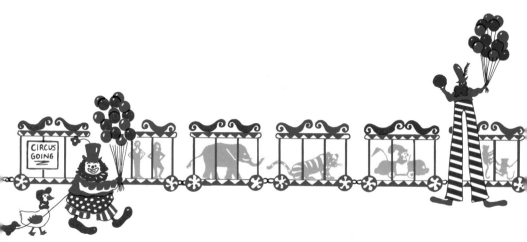

Peter Piper picked a peck of pickled pepper;
A peck of pickled pepper Peter Piper picked;
If Peter Piper picked a peck of pickled pepper,
Where is the peck of pickled pepper Peter Piper picked?

ONE, TWO, BUCKLE MY SHOE

One, two, buckle my shoe;
Three, four, shut the door;
Five, six, pick up sticks;
Seven, eight, lay them straight;
Nine, ten, a good fat hen;

CIRCUS
GOING

Eleven, twelve, who will delve?
Thirteen, fourteen, maids a-courting;
Fifteen, sixteen, maids in the kitchen;
Seventeen, eighteen, maids a-waiting;
Nineteen, twenty, my plate's empty.

RING AROUND A ROSIE

Ring around a rosie,
A pocket full of posies,
Ashes, ashes,
We all fall down.

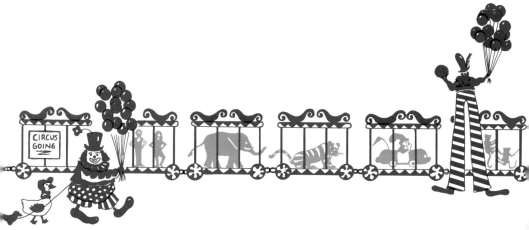

BOBBY SHAFTOE

Bobby Shaftoe's gone to sea,
Silver buckles on his knee;
He'll come back and marry me,
Bonny Bobby Shaftoe!
Bobby Shaftoe's young and fair,
Combing down his yellow hair,
He's my love forevermore,
Bonny Bobby Shaftoe.

CIRCUS COMING

SIMPLE SIMON

Simple Simon met a pieman
Going to the fair;
Says Simple Simon to the pieman,
"Let me taste your ware."

Says the pieman to Simple Simon
"Show me first your penny."
Says Simple Simon to the pieman,
"Indeed, I have not any."

CIRCUS
GOING

WEE WILLIE WINKLE

Wee Willie Winkle runs through the town,
Upstairs and downstairs, in his nightgown,
Rapping at the window, crying through the lock,
"Are your children in their beds?
For it's past eight o'clock."

THE DAYS OF THE MONTH

Thirty days hath September,
April, June and November;
February has twenty-eight alone,
All the rest have thirty-one,
Excepting leap-year, that's the time
When February's days are twenty-nine.

LOCK AND KEY

I am a gold lock; I am a gold key.
I am a silver lock; I am a silver key.
I am a brass lock; I am a brass key.
I am a lead lock; I am a lead key.
I am a monk lock; I am a monk key!

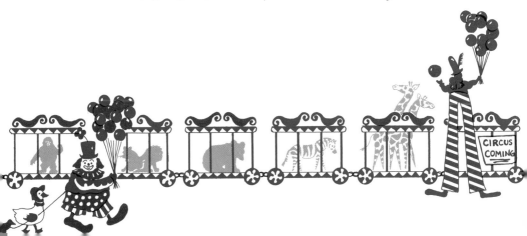

LONDON BRIDGE

London Bridge is falling down,
Falling down, falling down;
London Bridge is falling down,
My fair lady.

You stole my watch and kept my keys,
Kept my keys, kept my keys,
You stole my watch and kept my keys,
My fair lady.

CIRCUS
GOING

Off to prison she must go,
She must go, she must go;
Off to prison she must go,
    My fair lady.

Take the key and lock her up,
Lock her up, lock her up;
Take the key and lock her up,
    My fair lady.

LITTLE MISS MUFFET

Little Miss Muffet sat on a tuffet,
Eating her curds and whey;
Along came a spider and sat down beside her,
And frightened Miss Muffet away.

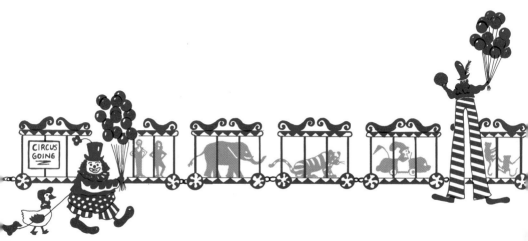

ROSES ARE RED

Roses are red, violets blue
Sugar is sweet, and so are you.
These are the words you bade me say
For a pair of gloves on Easter day.

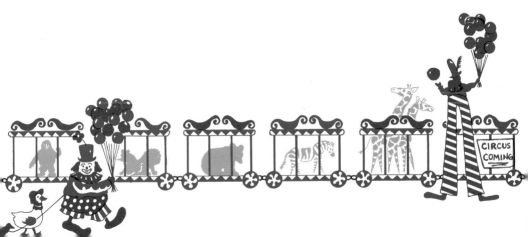

BAA, BAA BLACK SHEEP

Baa, baa, black sheep, have you any wool?
Yes, sir, yes, sir, three bags full:
One for the master, one for the dame,
And one for the little boy who lives down the lane.

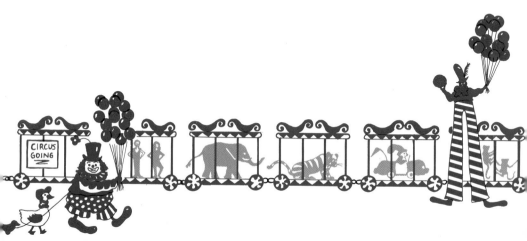

LITTLE BO-PEEP

Little Bo-Peep has lost her sheep,
And can't tell where to find them;
Leave them alone, and they'll come home,
Wagging their tails behind them.

SING A SONG OF SIXPENCE

Sing a song of sixpence,
A pocket full of rye;
Four and twenty blackbirds baked in a pie.
When the pie was opened
The birds began to sing,
Oh, wasn't that a dainty dish
To set before the King?

AS I WAS GOING TO ST. IVES

As I was going to St. Ives
I met a man with seven wives;
Each wife had seven sacks,
In each sack were seven cats,
And each cat had seven kits.
Kits, cats, sacks, and wives,
How many were going to St. Ives?

TOM, TOM THE PIPER'S SON

Tom, Tom, the piper's son,
Stole a pig, and away he run;
The pig was eat and Tom was beat,
And Tom ran crying down the street.

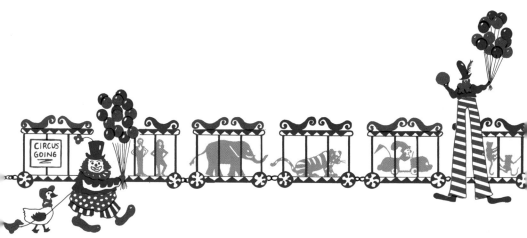

LUCY LOCKET

Lucy Locket lost her pocket,
Kitty Fisher found it;
Never a penny was there in it,
Save the binding round it.

HIGGLEDY, PIGGLEDY

Higgledy, piggledy, my black hen,
She lays eggs for gentlemen;
Gentlemen come every day
To see what my black hen does lay.

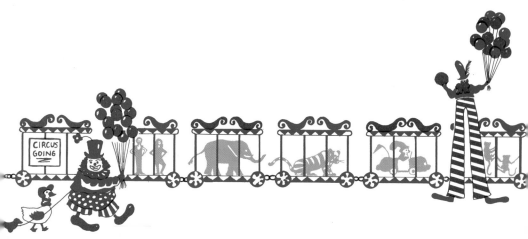

LITTLE TOMMY TUCKER

Little Tommy Tucker
Sing for your supper:
What shall I eat?
White bread and butter.
How shall I cut it
Without any knife?
How shall I marry without any wife?

MARY, MARY, QUITE CONTRARY

Mary, Mary, quite contrary.
How does your garden grow?
With silver bells and cockle shells
And pretty maids all in a row.

JACK, BE NIMBLE

Jack, be nimble,
Jack, be quick,
Jack jump over the candlestick.

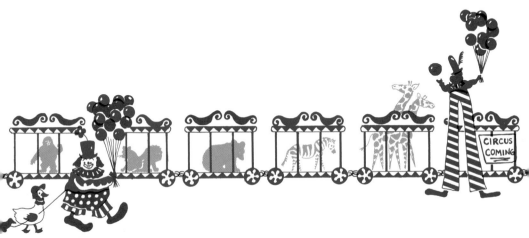

THERE WAS A CROOKED MAN

There was a crooked man, and he went a crooked mile;
He found a crooked sixpence against a crooked stile;
He bought a crooked cat, which caught a crooked mouse;
They all lived together in a little crooked house.

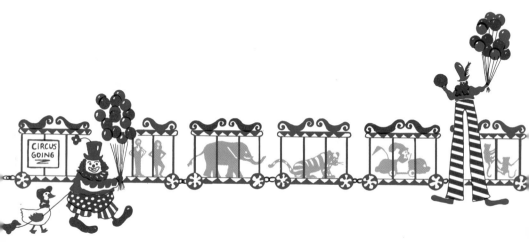

PEASE PORRIDGE HOT

Pease porridge hot,
Pease porridge cold,
Pease porridge in the pot
Nine days old.

HICKORY, DICKORY, DOCK

Hickory, dickory, dock;
The mouse ran up the clock;
The clock struck one,
The mouse ran down,
Hickory, dickory, dock.

DANCE, LITTLE BABY

Dance little baby, dance up high,
Never mind baby, Mother is by;
Crow and caper, caper and crow,
There, little baby, there you go;
Up to the ceiling,
down to the ground,
Backwards and forwards,
round and round.

THERE WAS AN OLD WOMAN

There was an old woman who lived in a shoe,
With so many children she didn't know what to do;
She gave them some broth with a nice piece of bread
And kissed them all roundly and sent them to bed.

Z IS A ZEBRA

Z is a zebra,
Whom you've heard of before;
So here ends my rhyme
Till I find you some more.

THE END